NATURE STORIES

Robin B. Cano

Helen Snell Neumeyer

Bee Thorpe

James Moffett, Senior Editor

Houghton Mifflin Company • Boston

Atlanta   Dallas   Geneva, Illinois   Hopewell, New Jersey   Palo Alto

Acknowledgments:

"It Looked Like Spilt Milk," text and illustrations from *It Looked Like Spilt Milk*, by Charles G. Shaw. Reprinted/recorded by permission of Harper & Row, Publishers.

"Spiders Are Spinners" by Ellsworth Rosen, excerpt used by permission of Houghton Mifflin Company.

"Bee and Dirtdauber," reprinted from *American Negro Folktales*, compiled by Richard M. Dorson, by permission of Premier Books, Fawcett Publications, Inc. Copyright © 1956, 1957 by Richard Mercer Dorson. Copyright © 1958 Indiana University Press.

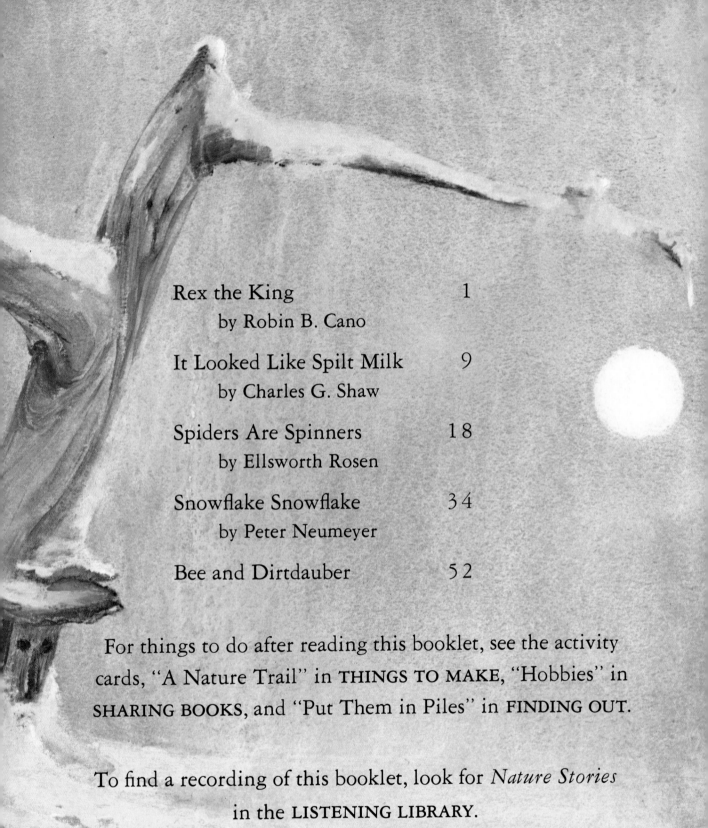

For things to do after reading this booklet, see the activity cards, "A Nature Trail" in THINGS TO MAKE, "Hobbies" in SHARING BOOKS, and "Put Them in Piles" in FINDING OUT.

To find a recording of this booklet, look for *Nature Stories* in the LISTENING LIBRARY.

REX
THE
KING

by Robin B. Cano

Rex was big.

Rex was tall.

He was taller than a giraffe.

He was as tall as a small house.

1

Rex had little legs in front.

He had big legs in back.

He had a long, strong tail.

Rex ate meat.

He had long, sharp teeth.

He killed other animals
to get meat to eat.

3

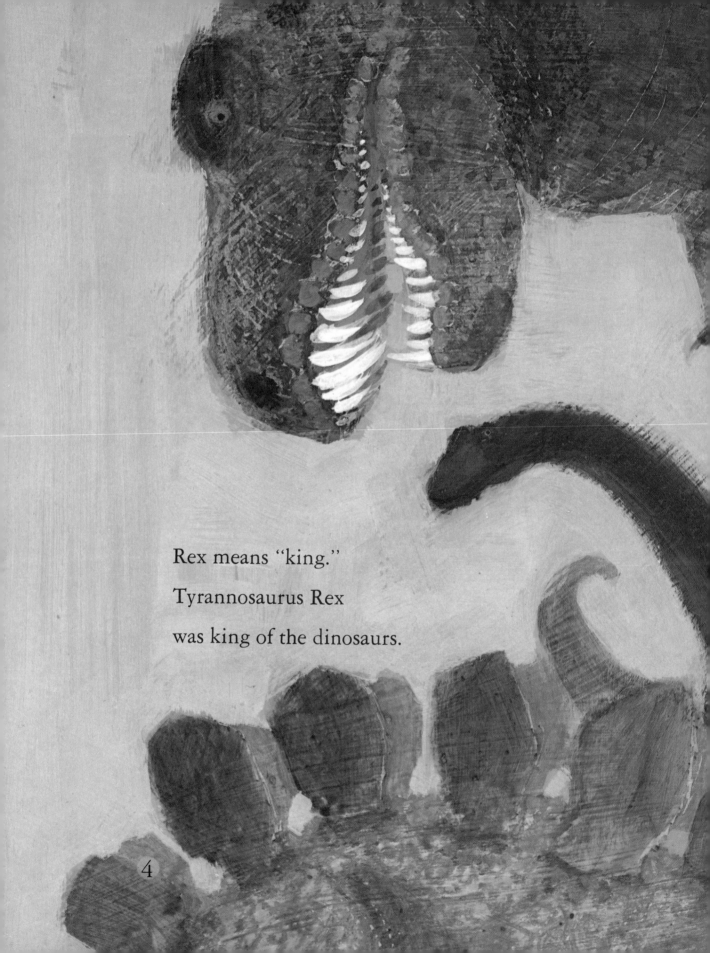

Rex means "king."
Tyrannosaurus Rex
was king of the dinosaurs.

4

6

Rex lived a long, long time ago.

Rex lived long before the cavemen.

Dinosaur bones have been found.

Dinosaur eggs have been found too.

These eggs and bones have
turned to stone.

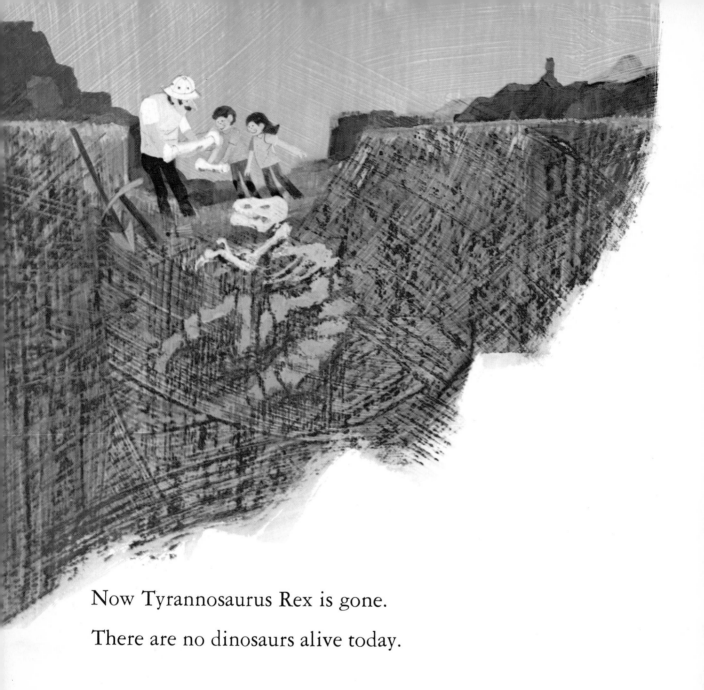

Now Tyrannosaurus Rex is gone.

There are no dinosaurs alive today.

It Looked Like Spilt Milk

by Charles G. Shaw

Sometimes it looked
like Spilt Milk.
But it wasn't Spilt Milk.

Sometimes it looked
like a Rabbit.
But it wasn't a Rabbit.

Sometimes it looked
like a Bird.
But it wasn't a Bird.

Sometimes it looked
like a Tree.
But it wasn't a Tree.

12

Sometimes it looked
	like an Ice Cream Cone.
But it wasn't an Ice Cream Cone.

13

Sometimes it looked
like a Pig.
But it wasn't a Pig.

14

Sometimes it looked
like a Birthday Cake.
But it wasn't a Birthday Cake.

Sometimes it looked
like Spilt Milk.
But it wasn't Spilt Milk.

It was just a Cloud in the Sky.

17

SPIDERS
ARE
SPINNERS

by Ellsworth Rosen

If you look in a corner

Or under a stair,

You'll see very often

A sticky web there.

You know, without guessing,

A spider has done it,

But do you know why and how it has spun it?

19

There's more to find out
About spiders than spinning,
And where you should start
Is, of course, the beginning.

Although they're not pretty,

Don't let them alarm you,

For most of the time

No spider will harm you.

They don't like to bite you,

Because you're no treat.

Mosquitoes and beetles are better to eat!

Spiders catch insects
That fly and that crawl;
So spiders, you see,
are your friends after all.

22

There are all kinds of spiders . . .

Dozens of dozens

Daddy longlegs and crabs

Are some of their cousins.

Why do you think
That most spiders are spinners?
To help them catch insects
For breakfasts and dinners.

Almost always at night, and without any sound,
The spiders will spin out the threads
'Round and 'round.
Their body makes something inside them like milk,
That almost like magic will turn into silk.

The threads keep on coming
As if on a reel,
And sometimes they're stretched
Like the spokes of a wheel.

Try to imagine how strong the threads are.
If they were a rope,
They could pick up a car.

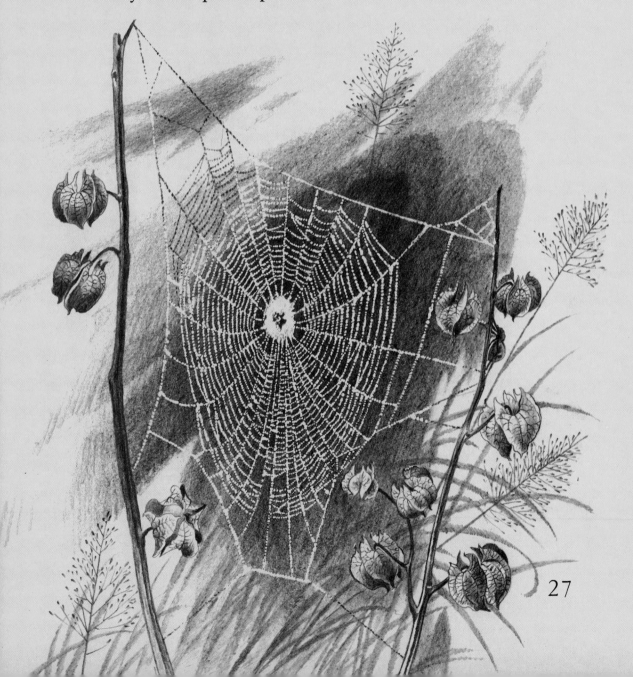

28

You'll often see bushes with webs like a sheet.
But some webs are messy
And not at all neat.

Some webs are bunched up
In corners of rooms,
And mothers who see them
Will go get their brooms.

The webs are quite sticky;
They're covered with glue,
And bugs that are caught
Can't get out or get through.

The spiders then tie them with threads
Rather neat;
They wrap them like gifts
From their head to their feet.

Spiders can walk on their webs
And don't stick.
Their secret is oil
That makes their feet slick.

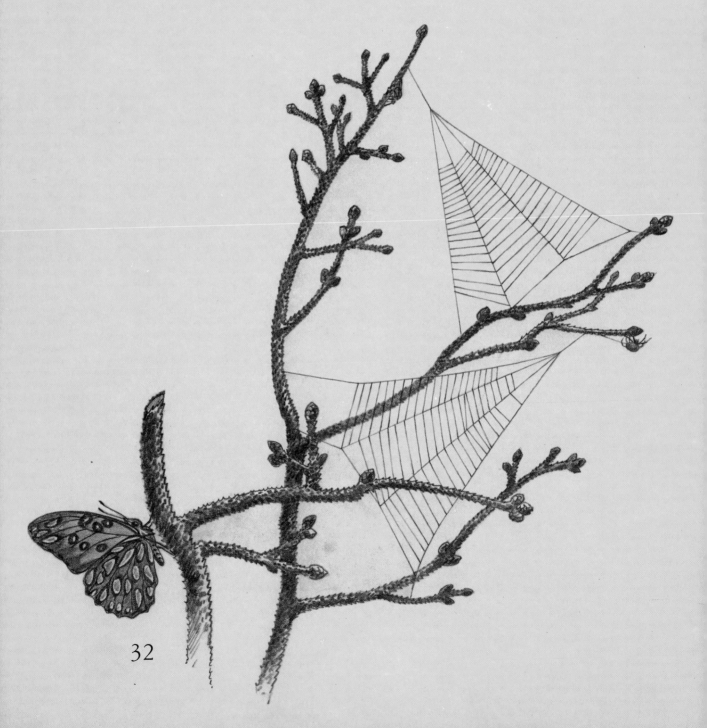

32

The thread of this story
Has spun to the end,
But there's much more to learn
And time you could spend.
To see all you can,
Keep your eyes open wider
Next time you notice a web or a spider.

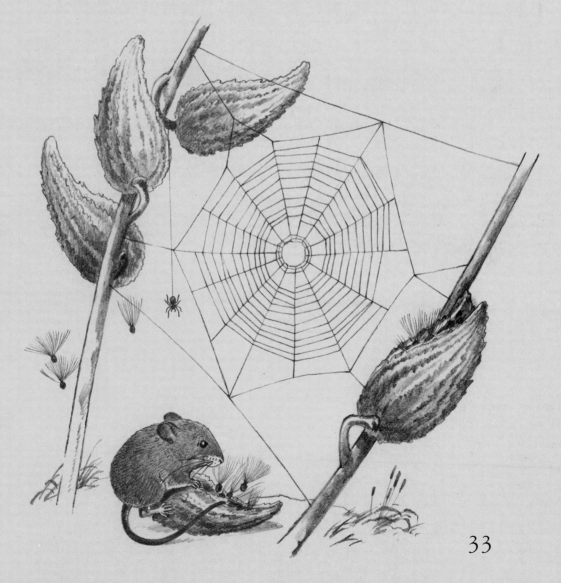

33

SNOWFLAKE SNOWFLAKE

by Peter Neumeyer

"Impossible, impossible, impossible," said
Andrew's father. "Never, never, anywhere in the world
can you find two snowflakes that are exactly alike."

35

"Not somewhere?" asked Andrew.

"Not anywhere," said his father.

"I've seen them exactly the same size," said
Andrew.

"Size is not everything," said his father.

"I've seen them the same shape," said Andrew.

"Shape is not everything," said his father. "And if they were the same shape, then they were probably not the same size."

"What if they were the same shape and the same size?" asked Andrew.

"If two snowflakes were the same shape and the same size — and that would be strange indeed — one would be more wet than the other. Or one would be more dry than the other."

"Nowhere?

    ever?

        are you sure?" asked Andrew.

"Nowhere, ever, I am sure," said his father.

39

Andrew got ready.

He took his magnifying glass.

He took his small jam glass.

He took his toothpick.

He put on his galoshes

his warmest coat

his mittens

and he went out in the storm.

The blizzard blew. Black tree ribs cracked with
the ice. The sun was in another place. And it was cold,
cold.

Even in mittens, Andrew's hands were frozen and
numb. His hands were clumsy. He could not really bend
his fingers. But ever so carefully with his toothpick
Andrew picked up one snowflake
then another.

He looked at them carefully — there in the cold
— through his magnifying glass.

The second snowflake was right. It was beautiful, small, and its points had their own points. Its outline was sharp, and Andrew could tell just exactly what it looked like. There was no question. No question at all. Though there was no sun, the snowflake glowed green, gold, blue, orange. It was so clear. It was beautiful.

Gently, with the toothpick, Andrew put his snowflake in the small jam glass.

Andrew knew his snowflake perfectly. He took it to his house. He set the small jam glass carefully just inside the front door of his house.

Again Andrew went out in the blizzard, in the snow.

Cold as he was, Andrew went looking, catching the blowing, swirling, falling snowflakes on his mitten. He could hardly see, it snowed so hard.

Andrew's nose felt frozen to him, and his eyelashes were heavy white with snow, but Andrew worked on. He looked at the snowflakes on his mitten through his magnifying glass.

Some were stuck together. Some had broken points, and some seemed to have none.

A few were ALMOST right — but they did not glow green, gold, blue, and orange. At least, not all those colors at once.

Andrew was so cold he could stay no longer. One last swirl he caught on his mitten.

"This will be my last chance," said Andrew, brushing off some of the snow and looking as carefully as he could through his magnifying glass at nine snowflakes on his mitten.

For a second — just a second — a sunbeam
glowed like icy fire. And there Andrew saw it, there on
his mitten, a snowflake

       beautiful

       small

       points on its points

       and glowing green, gold, blue, and orange.

Covering it, shielding the snowflake with his other mitten, Andrew rushed back, rushed home, out of the blizzard, back into his warm house, calling happily "Father, father . . . ."

51

Bee and Dirtdauber

A dirtdauber is just like a wasp, but he's black.
Some of 'em are brown. He makes up mud in his mouth
in a little ball, and holds it with his two front legs.
Then he carries it and sticks it up in any dry place that
has a hole in it — a house, a barn, a fence. He makes
him a house out of it, like a honeycomb.

53

Mrs. Dirtdauber went over to Mrs. Bee's house
to take dinner one day. Mrs. Bee had some good old
sweet honey for dinner. Mrs. Dirtdauber says, "Say,
Mrs. Bee, where did you get this at?"

Mrs. Bee said, "I made it."

"I sure wisht I could make that."

Mrs. Bee told her, "Be over here early in the morning before daylight, and come and go with me. I'll show you how to make this honey."

So off they goes to the mudhole, 'bout a mile through the woods, where Mrs. Bee gets her water. So the Bee lit right on the edge, and begin to suck her a little water.

Mrs. Dirtdauber, she begins to ball up mud, and tells Mrs. Bee, "I know, I know, I know."

So she flies back to the Bee's house, and begins her a comb. When she got it finished, there was no honey in the cells.

She said, "I know what I'll do. I'll just lay my eggs in the back end. Then I'll put a little thin coat of dirt between them and the food."

Next she puts spiders, and little bitty insects, in there and seals it up. Then the eggs hatch worms, and they eat the spiders till they're strong enough to bust out and care for theirselves.

She never did learn how to make honey, and never did go back to the Bee's house.

People's the same way. They won't wait to let you tell them —. "Oh, I know, I know," they say. Then they have a failure and put it on you.

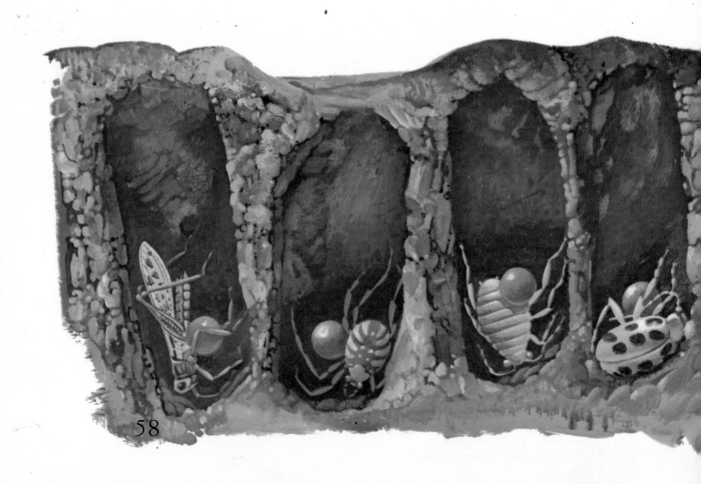

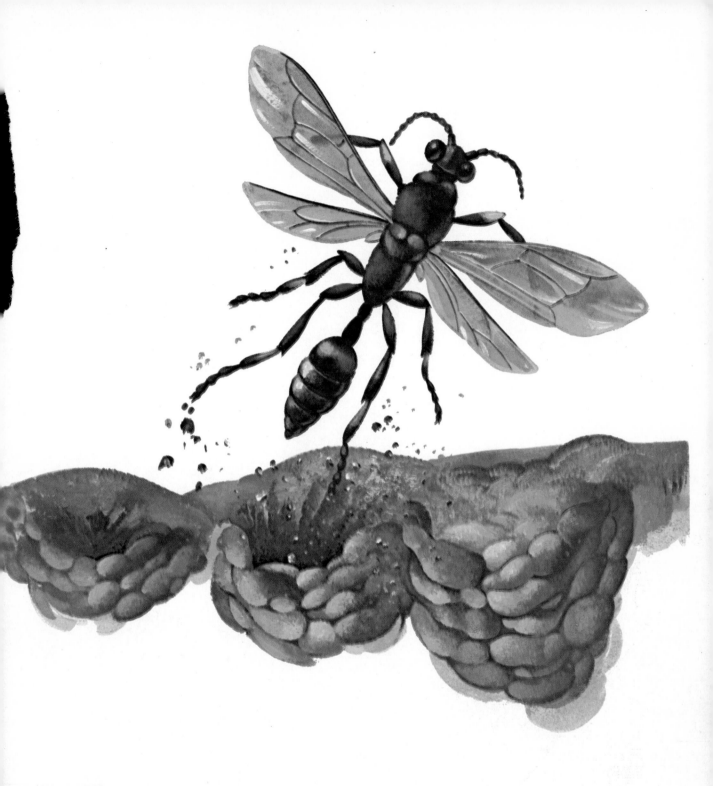

For Further Reading

Rain, Rain Rivers, *by Uri Shulevitz*

Big Tracks, Little Tracks, *by Franklyn M. Branley*

How High Is Up?, *by Bernice Kohn*

Time of Wonder, *by Robert McCloskey*

Illustrated by
Gil Riswold: Cover; pp. i–iii; "Snowflake Snowflake"
Tom Cooke: "Rex the King"
Charles G. Shaw: "Spilt Milk"
Teco Slagboom: "Spiders Are Spinners"
Charles Freeman: "Bee and Dirtdauber"

For things to do after reading this booklet, see the activity cards "A Nature Trail" in THINGS TO MAKE, "Hobbies" in SHARING BOOKS, and "Put Them in Piles" in FINDING OUT.

To find a recording of this booklet, look for *Nature Stories* in the LISTENING LIBRARY.